play guitar with
steely dan

bodhisattva
3

the boston rag
14

josie
20

kid charlemagne
26

reelin' in the years
34

rikki don't lose that number
44

guitar tablature explained
2

translations
52

Wise Publications
London/New York/Paris/Sydney/Copenhagen/Berlin/Madrid/Tokyo

guitar tablature explained

Guitar music can be notated three different ways: on a musical stave, in tablature, and in rhythm slashes

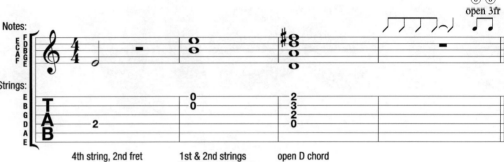

RHYTHM SLASHES are written above the stave. Strum chords in the rhythm indicated. Round noteheads indicate single notes.

THE MUSICAL STAVE shows pitches and rhythms and is divided by lines into bars. Pitches are named after the first seven letters of the alphabet.

TABLATURE graphically represents the guitar fingerboard. Each horizontal line represents a string, and each number represents a fret.

4th string, 2nd fret   1st & 2nd strings open, played together   open D chord

definitions for special guitar notation

SEMI-TONE BEND: Strike the note and bend up a semi-tone (1/2 step).

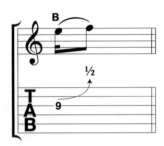

WHOLE-TONE BEND: Strike the note and bend up a whole-tone (whole step).

GRACE NOTE BEND: Strike the note and bend as indicated. Play the first note as quickly as possible.

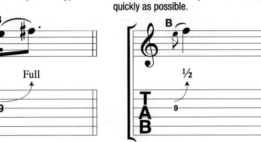

QUARTER-TONE BEND: Strike the note and bend up a 1/4 step.

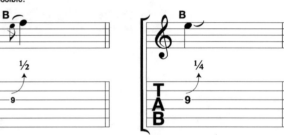

BEND & RELEASE: Strike the note and bend up as indicated, then release back to the original note.

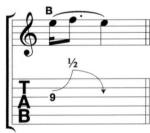

BEND & RESTRIKE: Strike the note and bend as indicated then restrike the string where the symbol occurs.

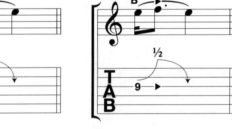

PRE-BEND: Bend the note as indicated, then strike it.

PRE-BEND & RELEASE: Bend the note as indicated. Strike it and release the note back to the original pitch.

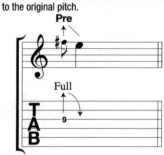

HAMMER-ON: Strike the first (lower) note with one finger, then sound the higher note (on the same string) with another finger by fretting it without picking.

PULL-OFF: Place both fingers on the notes to be sounded. Strike the first note and without picking, pull the finger off to sound the second (lower) note.

LEGATO SLIDE (GLISS): Strike the first note and then slide the same fret-hand finger up or down to the second note. The second note is not struck.

SHIFT SLIDE (GLISS & RESTRIKE): Same as legato slide, except the second note is struck.

NATURAL HARMONIC: Strike the note while the fret-hand lightly touches the string directly over the fret indicated.

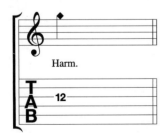

PICK SCRAPE: The edge of the pick is rubbed down (or up) the string, producing a scratchy sound.

PALM MUTING: The note is partially muted by the pick hand lightly touching the string(s) just before the bridge.

MUFFLED STRINGS: A percussive sound is produced by laying the fret hand across the string(s) without depressing, and striking them with the pick hand.

NOTE: The speed of any bend is indicated by the music notation and tempo.

bodhisattva

Words & Music by Walter Becker & Donald Fagen

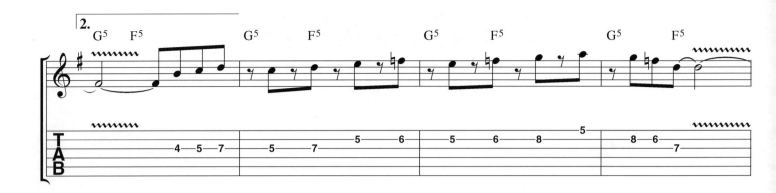

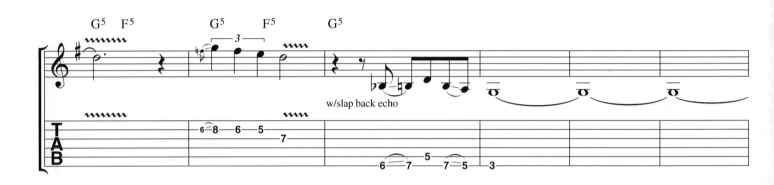

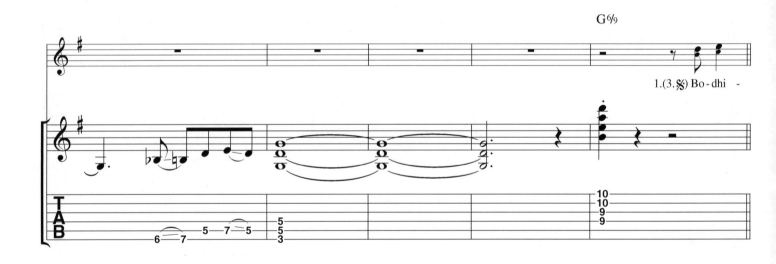

1.(3.𝄋) Bo - dhi -

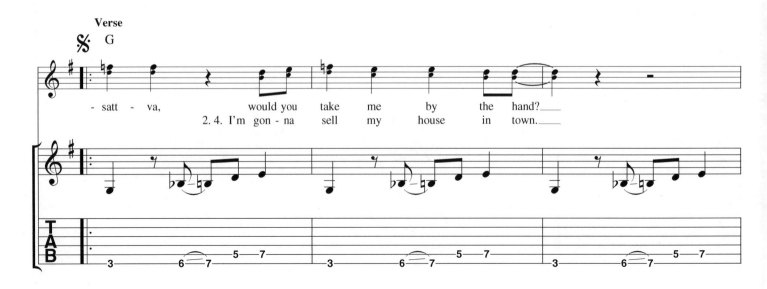

Verse

- satt - va,   would you   take   me   by   the   hand?___
2. 4. I'm gon - na   sell   my   house   in   town.___

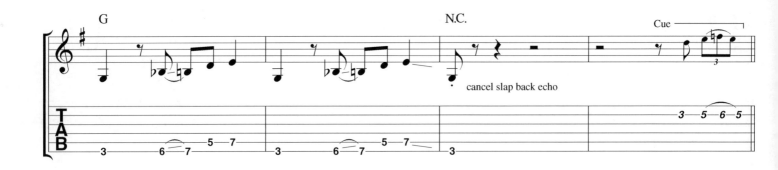

Solo

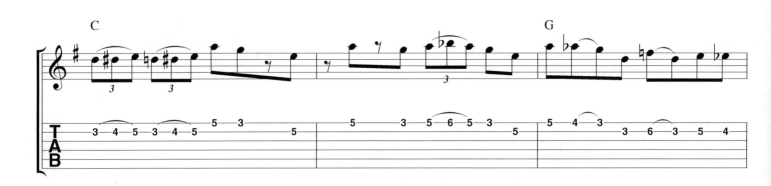

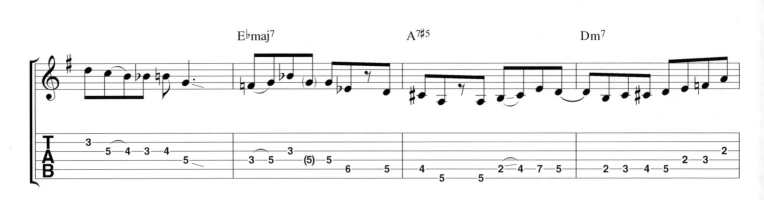

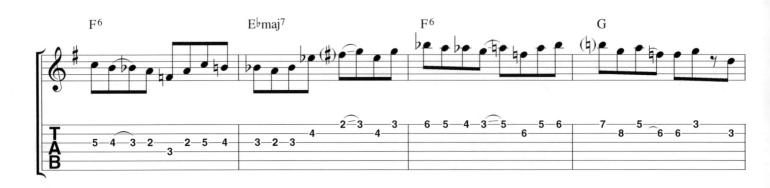

6

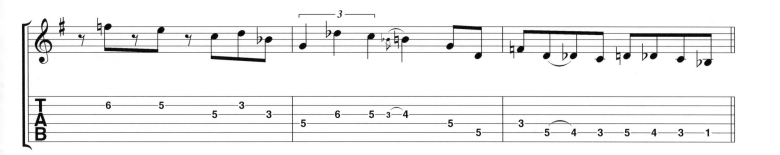

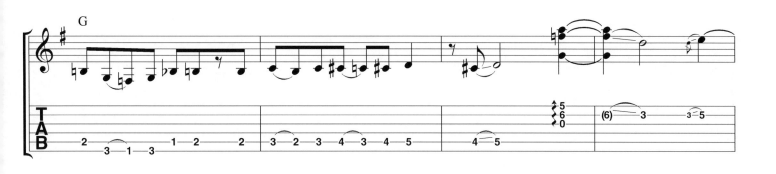

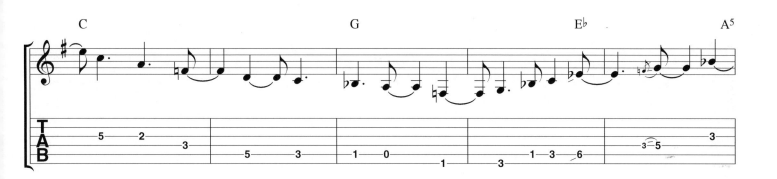

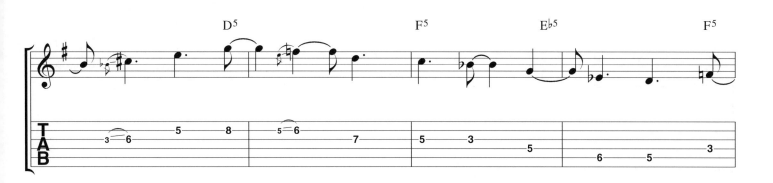

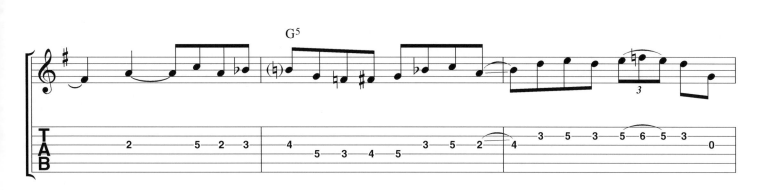

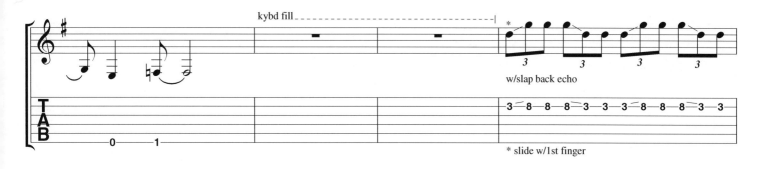

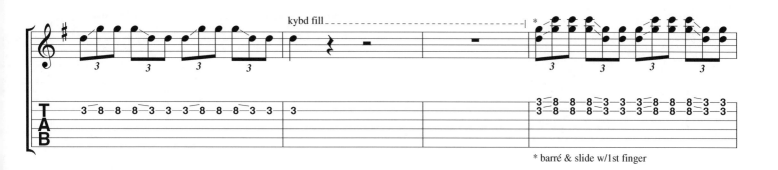

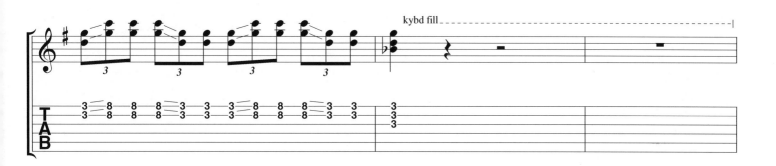

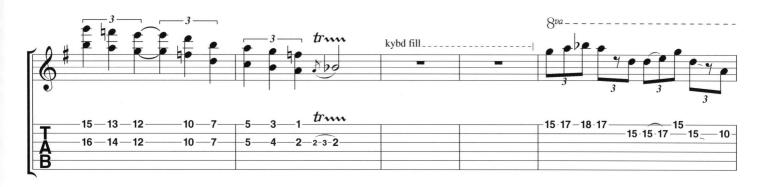

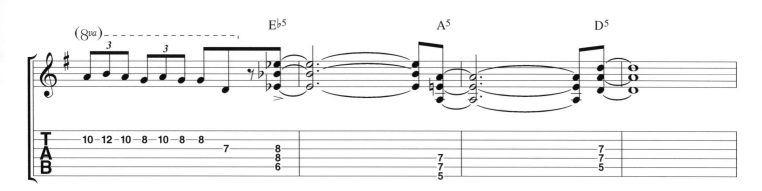

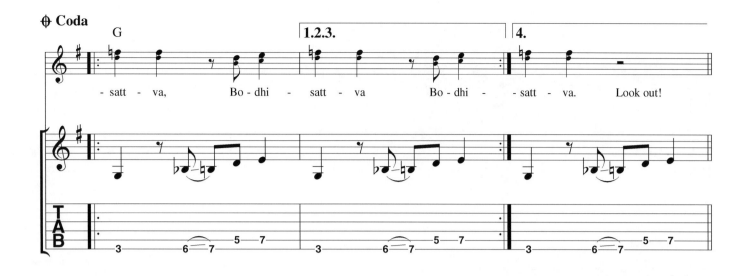

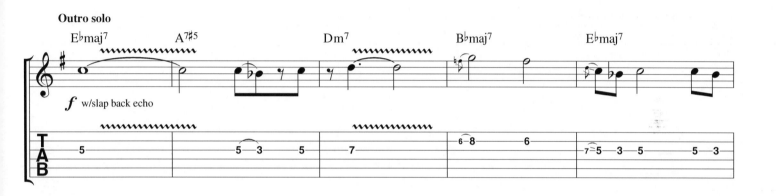

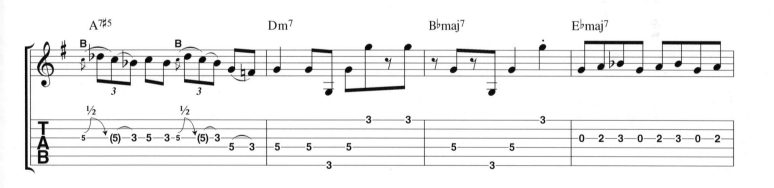

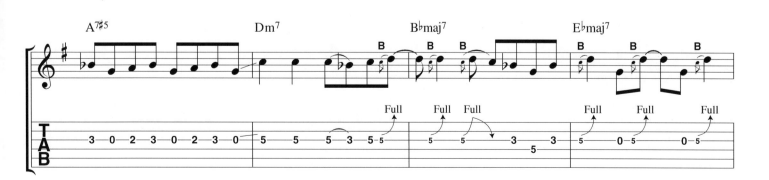

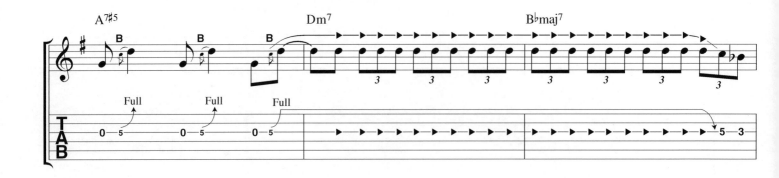

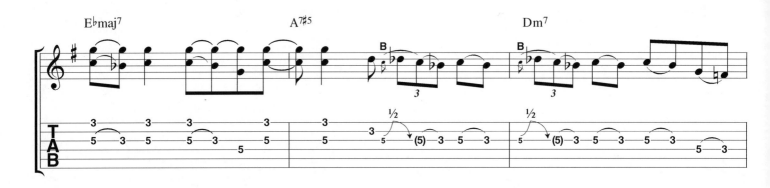

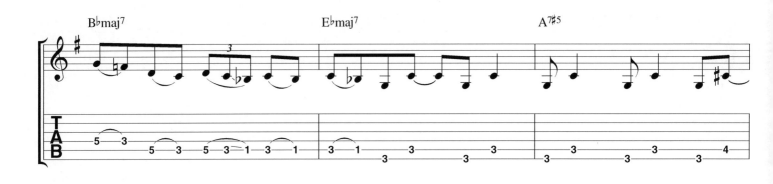

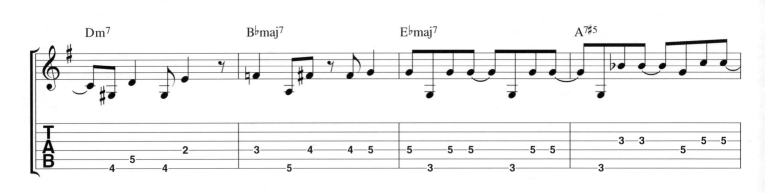

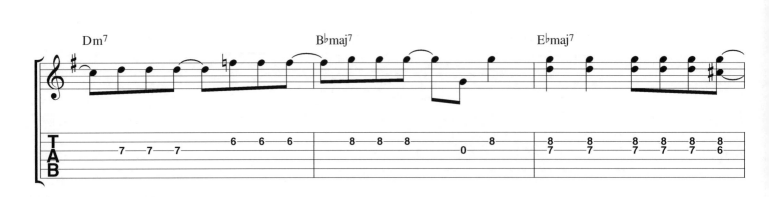

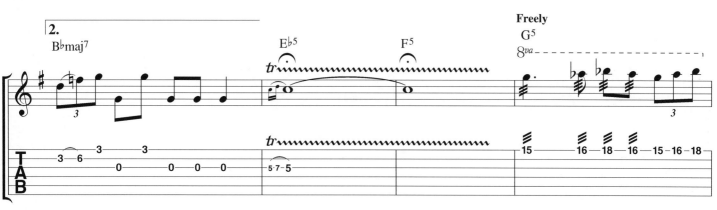

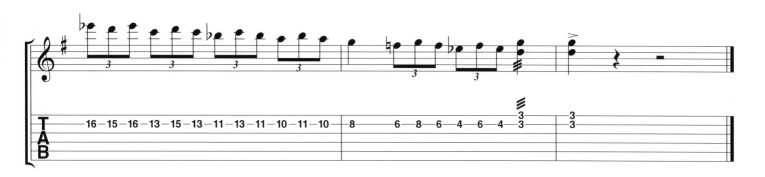

the boston rag

Words & Music by Walter Becker & Donald Fagen

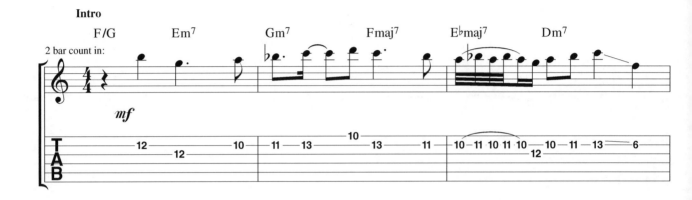

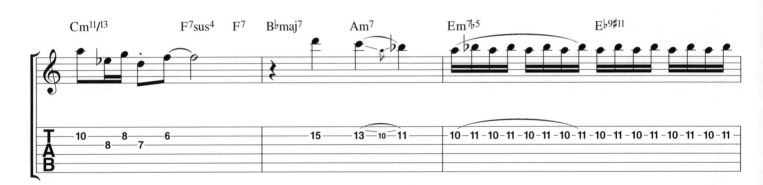

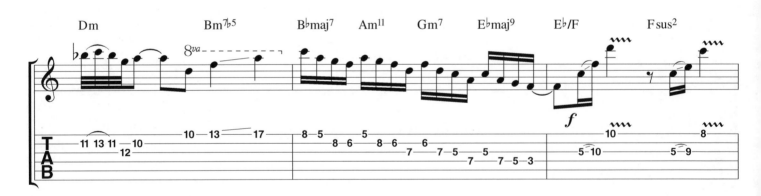

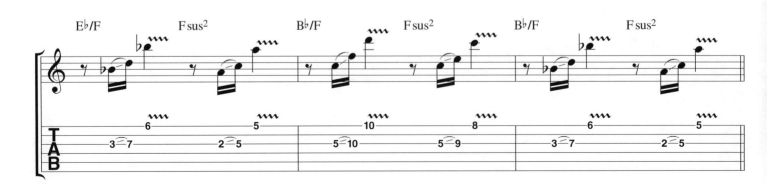

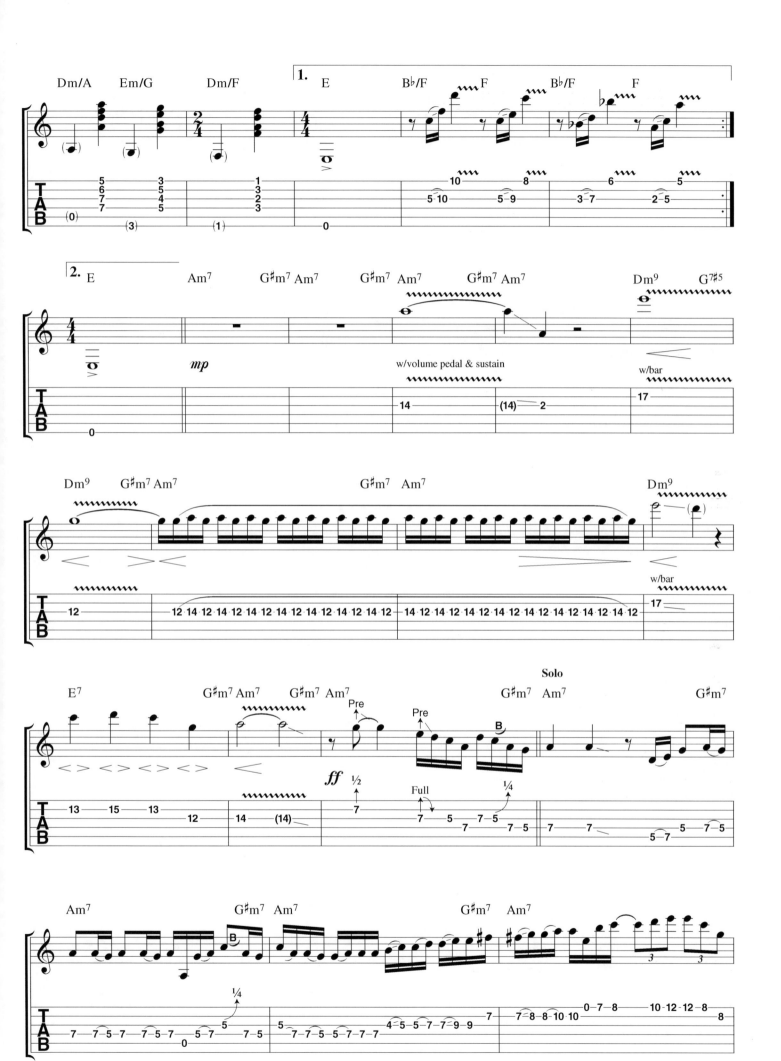

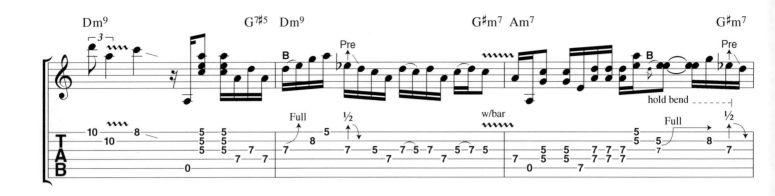

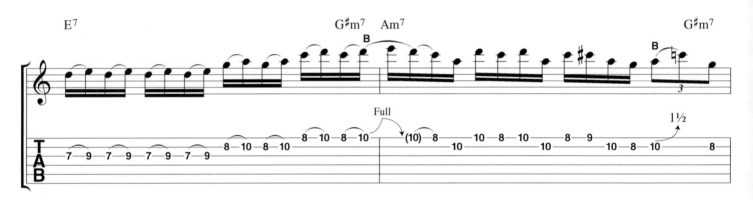

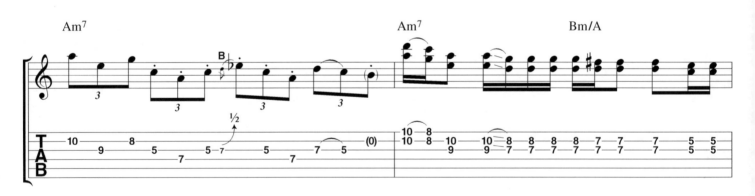

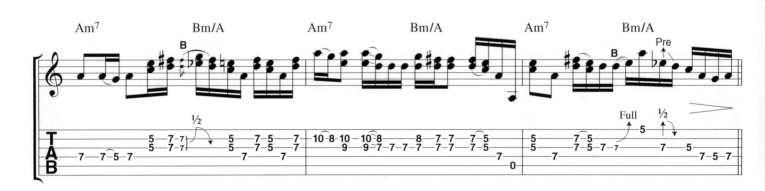

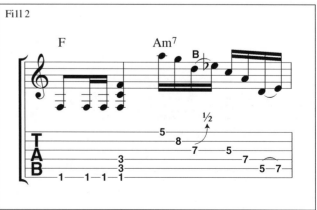

josie

Words & Music by Walter Becker & Donald Fagen

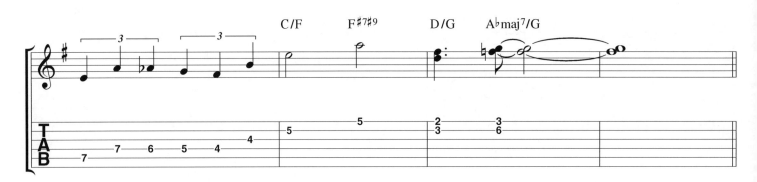

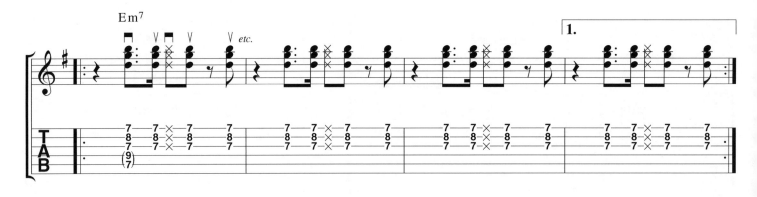

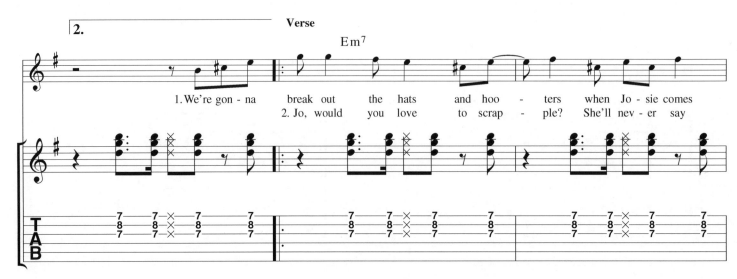

1.We're gon - na   break out   the hats   and hoo - ters   when Jo - sie comes
2.Jo, would   you love   to scrap - ple?   She'll nev - er say

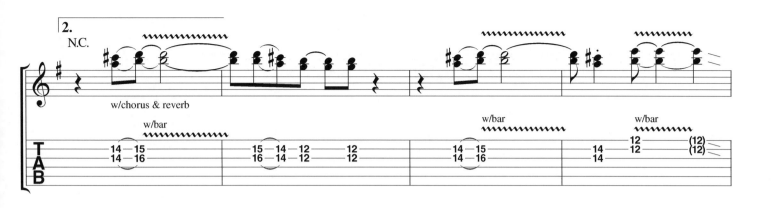

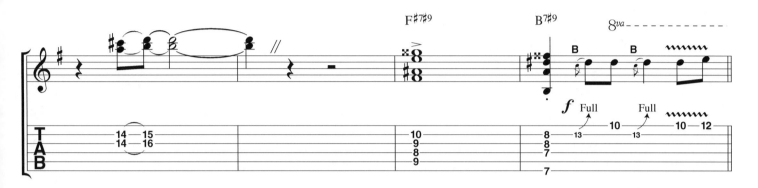

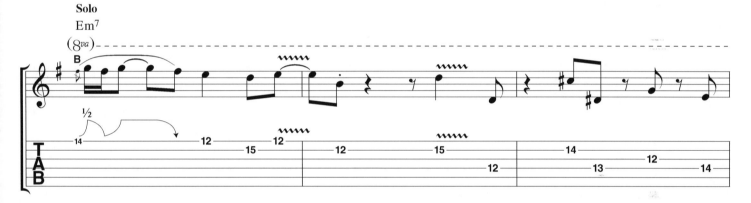

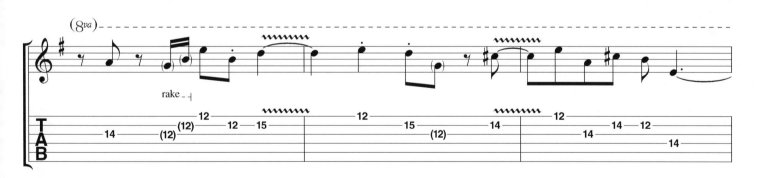

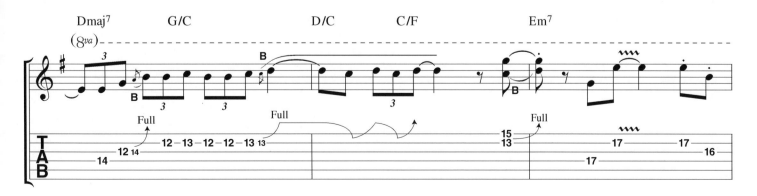

23

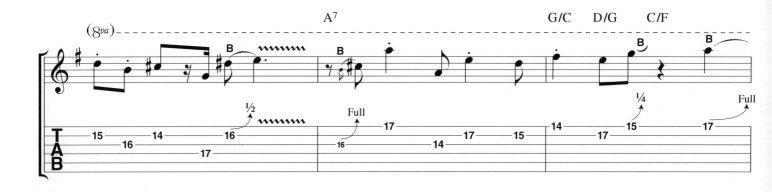

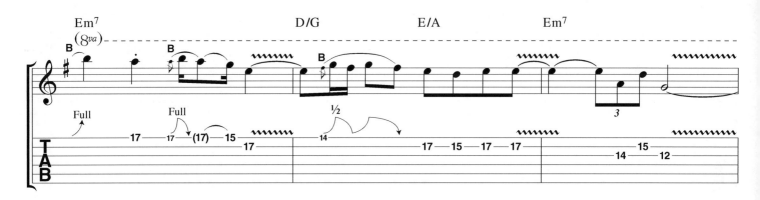

Chorus

When Jos - ie comes home so good.___ She's the pride

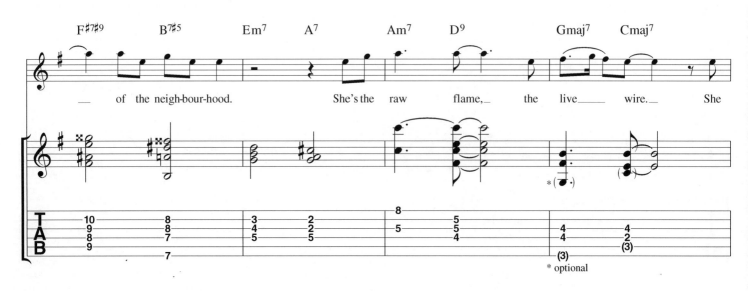

___ of the neigh-bour-hood. She's the raw flame,___ the live___ wire. She

* optional

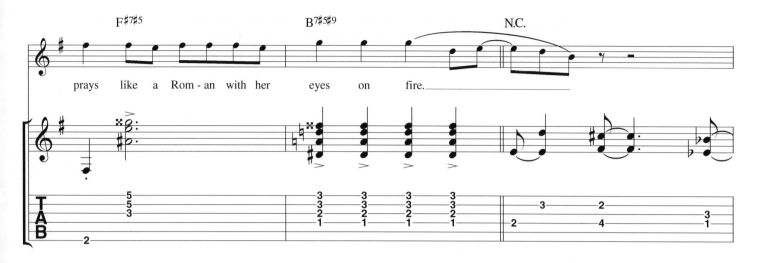

prays   like   a   Rom-an   with   her   eyes   on   fire.

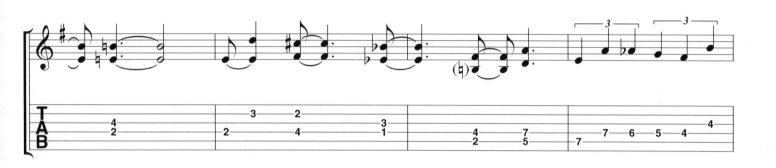

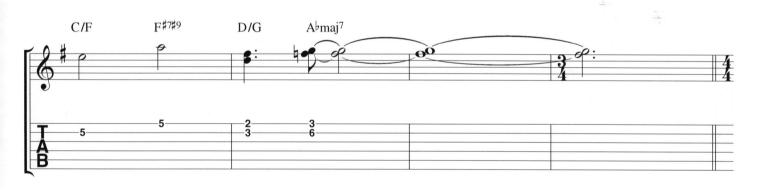

Outro

Repeat ad lib to fade

25

kid charlemagne

Words & Music by Walter Becker & Donald Fagen

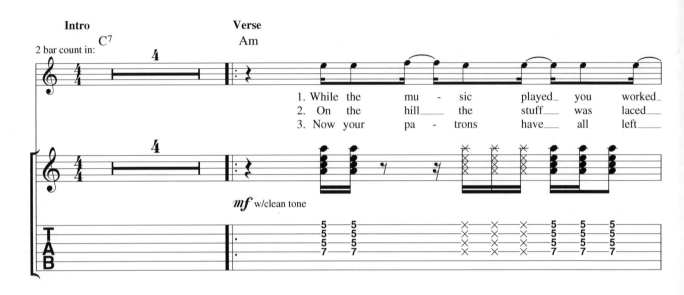

Lyrics:

1. While the mu-sic played you worked by can-dle light,__ those San Fran-cis-co nights, you were the best__ in town.__
2. On the hill the stuff__ was laced with ke-ro-sene,__ but yours was kit-chen clean. Ev-'ry-one stopped to stare at your tech-ni-col-our mo-tor home.
3. Now your pa-trons have__ all left you in the red,__ your low-rent friends are dead, this life can be very strange.

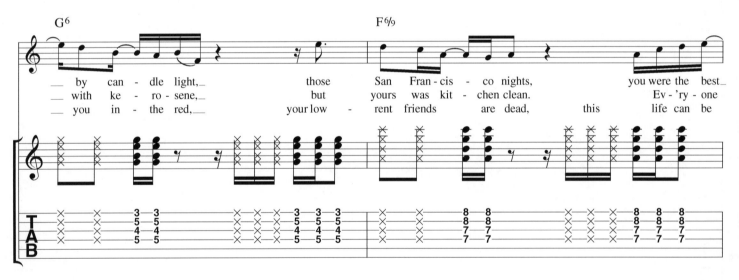

Just by chance__ you cross the dia-
Ev-'ry A-frame had your num-
All those day-glo freaks who used

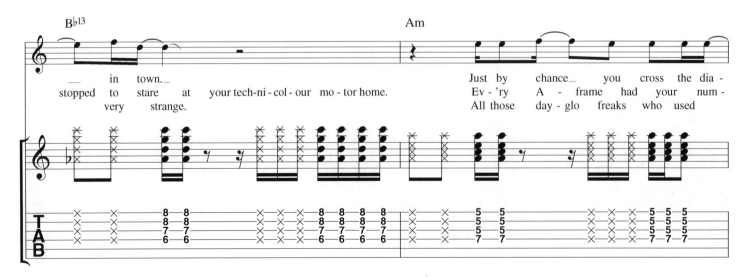

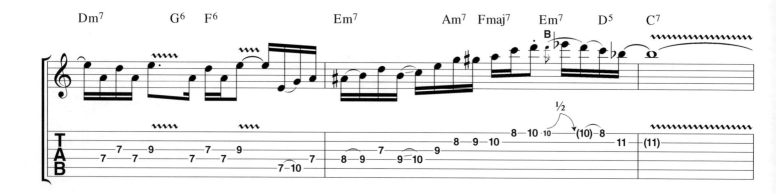

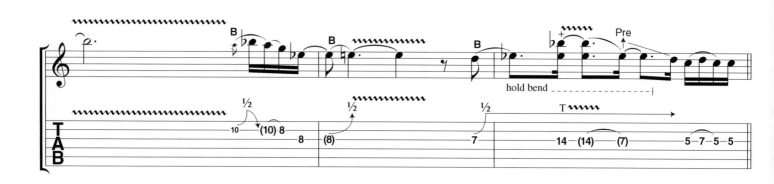

Verse

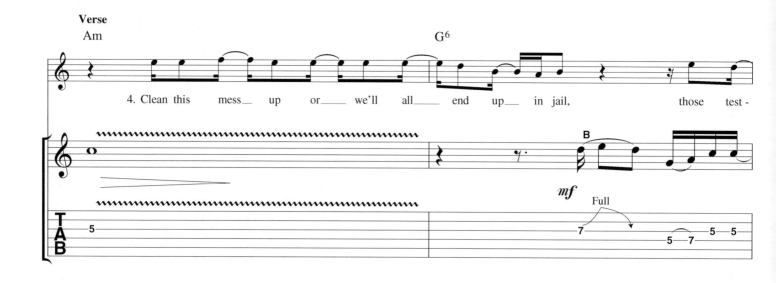

4. Clean this mess___ up or___ we'll all___ end up___ in jail, those test-

___ tubes and___ the scales, just___ get it all out of here.

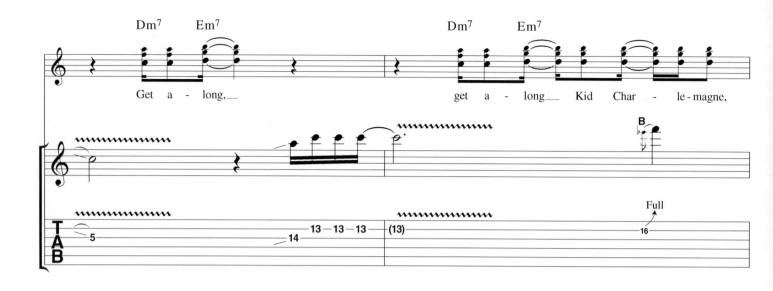

Get a - long,___ get a - long Kid Char - le - magne,

get a - long___ Kid Char - le - magne.___

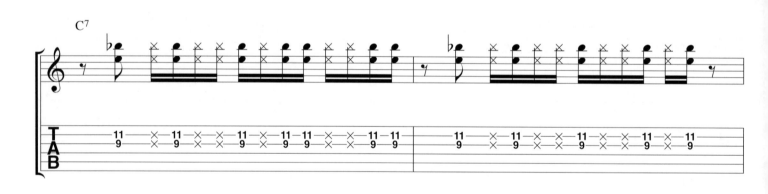

Outro solo

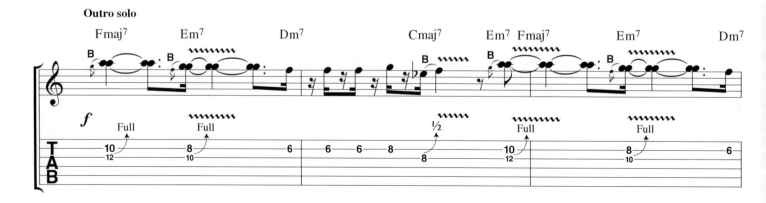

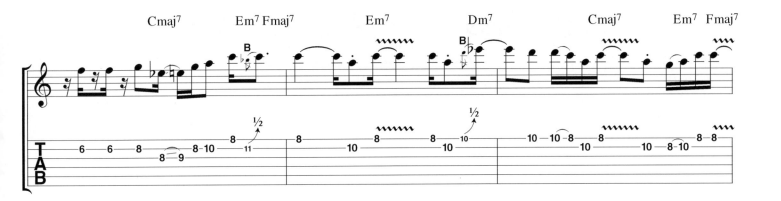

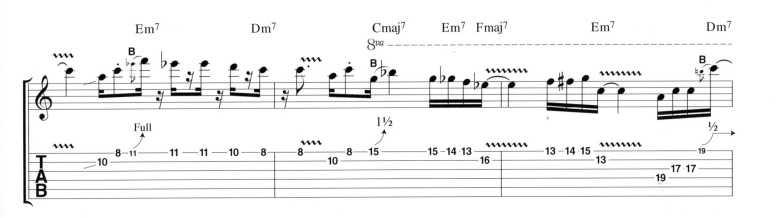

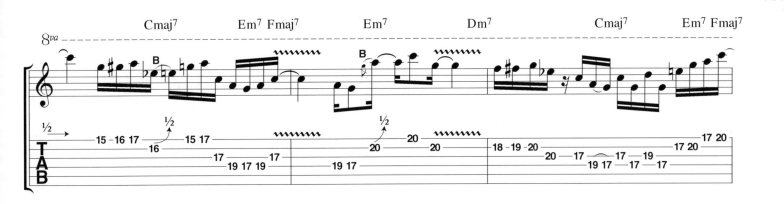

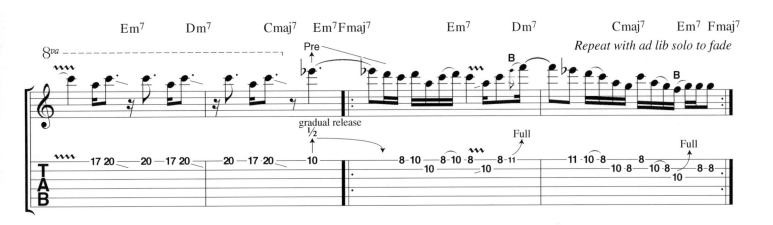

reelin' in the years

Words & Music by Walter Becker & Donald Fagen

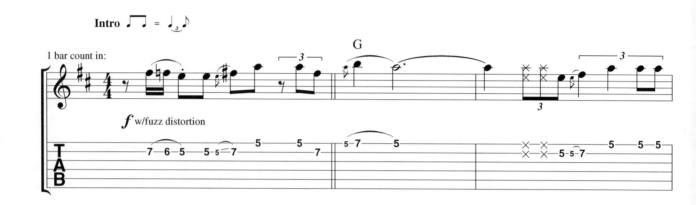

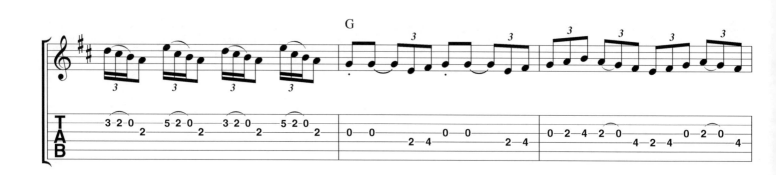

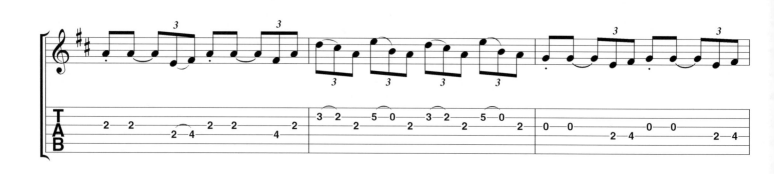

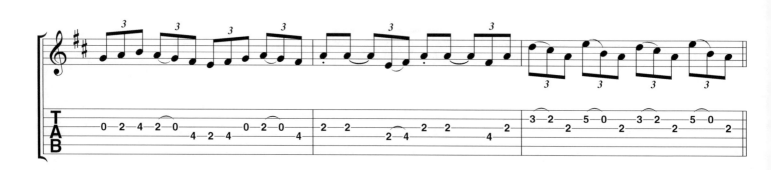

Solo

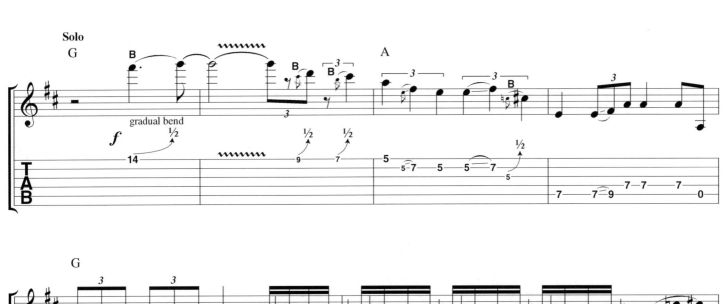

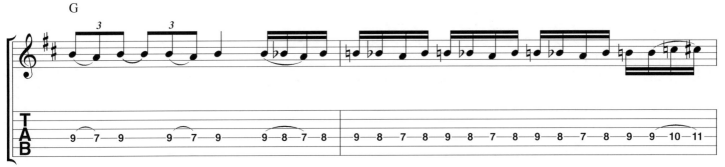

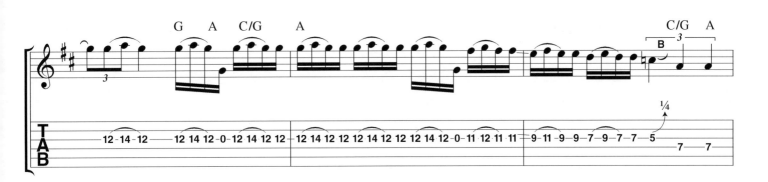

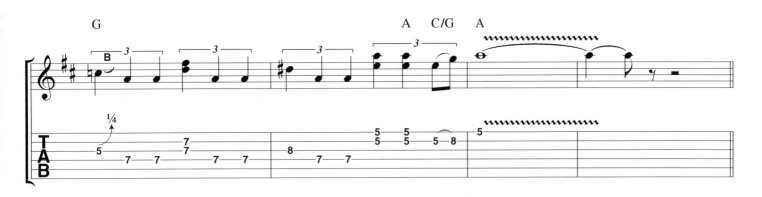

tears?_____   Have you had e - nough of   mine?_____

Outro solo

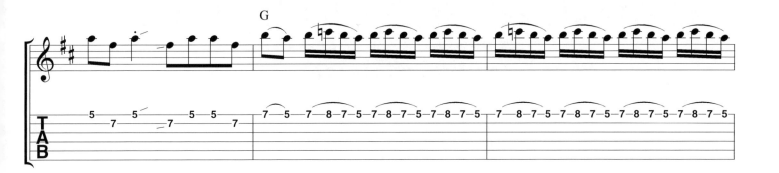

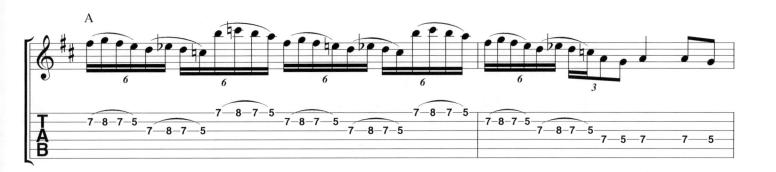

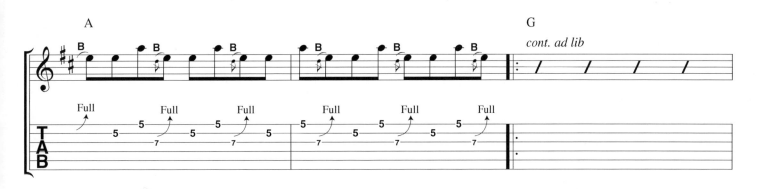

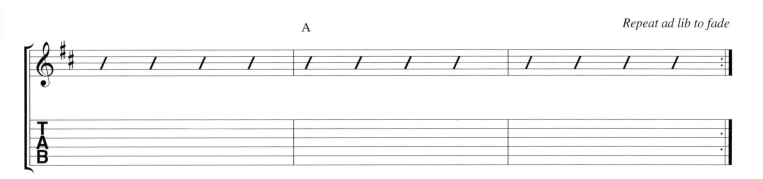

rikki don't lose that number

Words & Music by Walter Becker & Donald Fagen

Intro

Verse

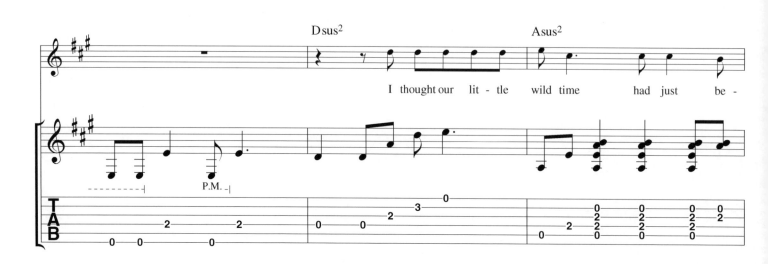

Chorus

And you could have a change of heart.

Rik - ki don't lose that num - ber, you don't want to call no - bod - y else.

Send it off in a let - ter to your - - - self.

Fill 1

48

Rik - ki don't lose that num - ber, it's the

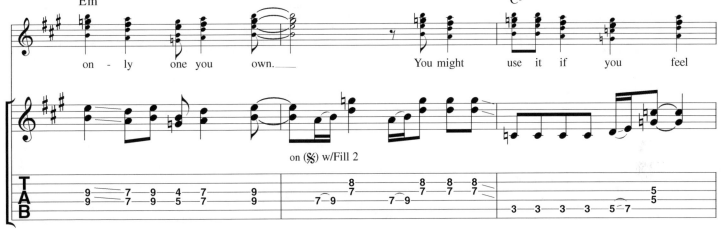

on - ly one you own. You might use it if you feel

on (𝄋) w/Fill 2

bet - ter, when you get__ home.

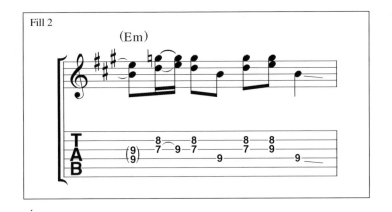

Fill 2

(Em)

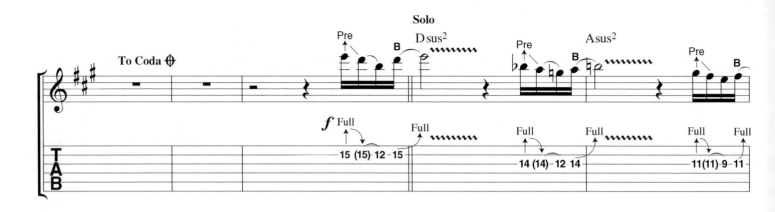

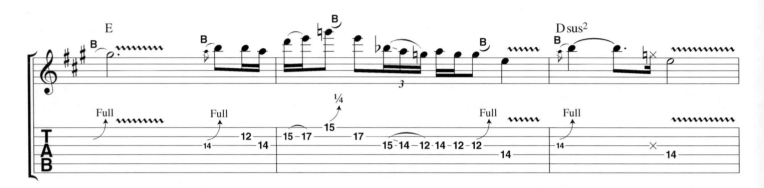

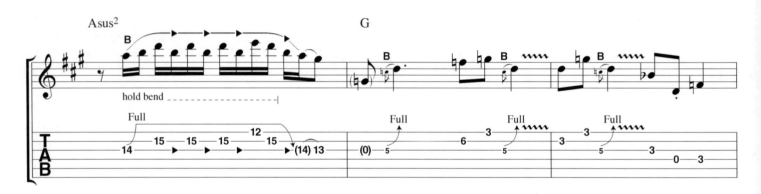

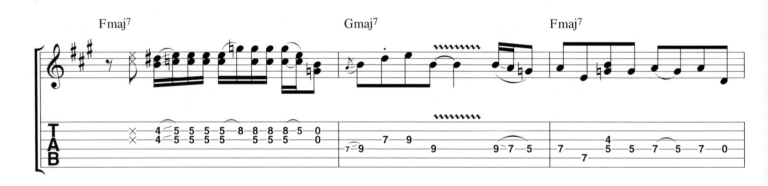

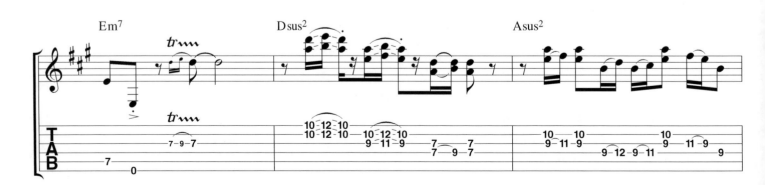

Présentation De La Tablature De Guitare

Il existe trois façons différentes de noter la musique pour guitare : à l'aide d'une portée musicale, de tablatures ou de barres rythmiques.

Les **BARRES RYTHMIQUES** sont indiquées au-dessus de la portée. Jouez les accords dans le rythme indiqué. Les notes rondes indiquent des notes réciles.

La **PORTÉE MUSICALE** indique les notes et rythmes et est divisée en mesures. Cette division est représentée par des lignes. Les notes sont : do, ré, mi, fa, sol, la, si.

La **PORTÉE EN TABLATURE** est une représentation graphique des touches de guitare. Chaque ligne horizontale correspond à une corde et chaque chiffre correspond à une case.

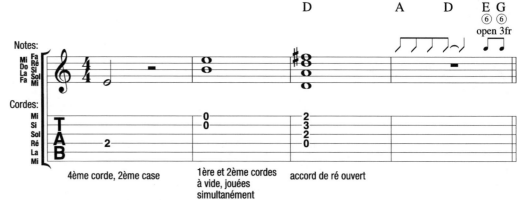

4ème corde, 2ème case   1ère et 2ème cordes à vide, jouées simultanément   accord de ré ouvert

Notation Spéciale De Guitare : Définitions

TIRÉ DEMI-TON : Jouez la note et tirez la corde afin d'élever la note d'un demi-ton (étape à moitié).

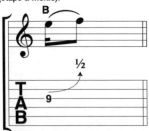

TIRÉ PLEIN : Jouez la note et tirez la corde afin d'élever la note d'un ton entier (étape entière).

TIRÉ D'AGRÉMENT : Jouez la note et tirez la corde comme indiqué. Jouez la première note aussi vite que possible.

TIRÉ QUART DE TON : Jouez la note et tirez la corde afin d'élever la note d'un quart de ton.

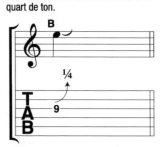

TIRÉ ET LÂCHÉ : Jouez la note et tirez la corde comme indiqué, puis relâchez, afin d'obtenir de nouveau la note de départ.

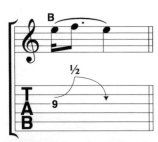

TIRÉ ET REJOUÉ : Jouez la note et tirez la corde comme indiqué puis rejouez la corde où le symbole apparaît.

PRÉ-TIRÉ : Tirez la corde comme indiqué puis jouez cette note.

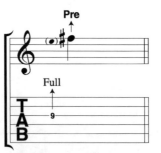

PRÉ-TIRÉ ET LÂCHÉ : Tirez la corde comme indiqué. Jouez la note puis relâchez la corde afin d'obtenir le ton de départ.

HAMMER-ON: Jouez la première note (plus basse) avec un doigt puis jouez la note plus haute sur la même corde avec un autre doigt, sur le manche mais sans vous servir du médiator.

PULL-OFF: Positionnez deux doigts sur les notes à jouer. Jouez la première note et sans vous servir du médiator, dégagez un doigt pour obtenir la deuxième note, plus basse.

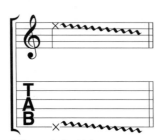

GLISSANDO : Jouez la première note puis faites glisser le doigt le long du manche pour obtenir la seconde note qui, elle, n'est pas jouée.

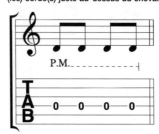

GLISSANDO ET REJOUÉ : Identique au glissando à ceci près que la seconde note est jouée.

HARMONIQUES NATURELLES : Jouez la note tandis qu'un doigt effleure la corde sur le manche correspondant à la case indiquée.

PICK SCRAPE (SCRATCH) : On fait glisser le médiator le long de la corde, ce qui produit un son éraillé.

ÉTOUFFÉ DE LA PAUME : La note est partiellement étouffée par la main (celle qui se sert du médiator). Elle effleure la (les) corde(s) juste au-dessus du chevalet.

CORDES ÉTOUFFÉES : Un effet de percussion produit en posant à plat la main sur le manche sans relâcher, puis en jouant les cordes avec le médiator.

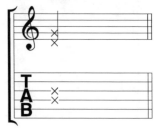

NOTE: La vitesse des tirés est indiquée par la notation musicale et le tempo.

Erläuterung zur Tabulaturschreibweise

Es gibt drei Möglichkeiten, Gitarrenmusik zu notieren: im klassischen Notensystem, in Tabulaturform oder als rhythmische Akzente.

RHYTHMISCHE AKZENTE werden über dem Notensystem notiert. Geschlagene Akkorde werden rhythmisch dargestellt. Ausgeschriebene Noten stellen Einzeltöne dar.

Im **NOTENSYSTEM** werden Tonhöhe und rhythmischer Verlauf festgelegt; es ist durch Taktstriche in Takte unterteilt. Die Töne werden nach den ersten acht Buchstaben des Alphabets benannt.
Beachte: "B" in der anglo-amerkanischen Schreibweise entspricht dem deutschen "H"!

DIE TABULATUR ist die optische Darstellung des Gitarrengriffbrettes. Jeder horizontalen Linie ist eine bestimmte Saite zugeordnet, jede Zahl bezeichnet einen Bund.

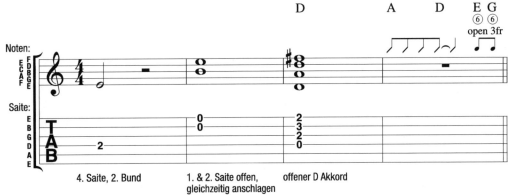

4. Saite, 2. Bund   1. & 2. Saite offen,   offener D Akkord
gleichzeitig anschlagen

Erklärungen zur speziellen Gitarennotation

HALBTON-ZIEHER: Spiele die Note und ziehe dann um einen Halbton höher (Halbtonschritt).

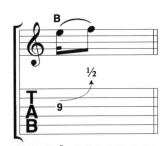

GANZTON-ZIEHER: Spiele die Note und ziehe dann einen Ganzton höher (Ganztonschritt).

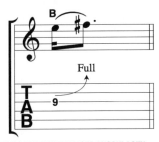

ZIEHER MIT VORSCHLAG: Spiele die Note und ziehe wie notiert. Spiele die erste Note so schnell wie möglich.

VIERTELTON-ZIEHER: Spiele die Note und ziehe dann einen Viertelton höher (Vierteltonschritt).

ZIEHEN UND ZURÜCKGLEITEN: Spiele die Note und ziehe wie notiert; lasse den Finger dann in die Ausgangposition zurückgleiten. Dabei wird nur die erste Note angeschlagen.

ZIEHEN UND NOCHMALIGES ANSCHLAGEN: Spiele die Note und ziehe wie notiert, schlage die Saite neu an, wenn das Symbol "▶" erscheint und lasse den Finger dann zurückgleiten.

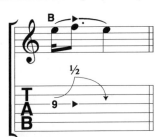

ZIEHER VOR DEM ANSCHLAGEN: Ziehe zuerst die Note wie notiert; schlage die Note dann an.

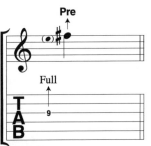

ZIEHER VOR DEM ANSCHLAGEN MIT ZURÜCKGLEITEN: Ziehe die Note wie notiert; schlage die Note dann an und lasse den Finger auf die Ausgangslage zurückgleiten.

AUFSCHLAGTECHNIK: Schlage die erste (tiefere) Note an; die höhere Note (auf der selben Saite) erklingt durch kräftiges Aufschlagen mit einem anderen Finger der Griffhand.

ABZIEHTECHNIK: Setze beide Finger auf die zu spielenden Noten und schlage die erste Note an. Ziehe dann (ohne nochmals anzuschlagen) den oberen Finger der Griffhand seitlich - abwärts ab, um die zweite (tiefere) Note zum klingen zu bringen.

GLISSANDOTECHNIK: Schlage die erste Note an und rutsche dann mit dem selben Finger der Griffhand aufwärts oder abwärts zur zweiten Note. Die zweite Note wird nicht angeschlagen.

GLISSANDOTECHNIK MIT NACHFOLGENDEM ANSCHLAG: Gleiche Technik wie das gebundene Glissando, jedoch wird die zweite Note angeschlagen.

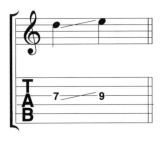

NATÜRLICHES FLAGEOLETT: Berühre die Saite über dem angegebenen Bund leicht mit einem Finger der Griffhand. Schlage die Saite an und lasse sie frei schwingen.

PICK SCRAPE: Fahre mit dem Plektrum nach unten über die Saiten - klappt am besten bei umsponnenen Saiten.

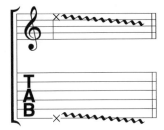

DÄMPFEN MIT DER SCHLAGHAND: Lege die Schlaghand oberhalb der Brücke leicht auf die Saite(n).

DÄMPFEN MIT DER GRIFFHAND: Du erreichst einen percussiven Sound, indem du die Griffhand leicht über die Saiten legst (ohne diese herunterzudrücken) und dann mit der Schlaghand anschlägst.

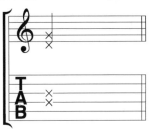

AMMERKUNG: Das Tempo der Zieher und Glissandos ist abhängig von der rhythmischen Notation und dem Grundtempo.

Spiegazioni Di Tablatura Per Chitarra

La musica per chitarra può essere annotata in tre diversi modi: sul pentagramma, in tablatura e in taglio ritmico

IL TAGLIO RITMICO è scritto sopra il pentagramma. Percuotere le corde al ritmo indicato Le teste arrotondate delle note indicano note singole.

IL PENTAGRAMMA MUSICALE mostra toni e ritmo ed è divisa da linee in settori. I toni sono indicati con le prime sette lettere dell'alfabeto.

LA TABLATURA rappresenta graficamente la tastiera della chitarra. Ogni linea orizzontale rappresenta una corda, ed ogni corda rappresenta un tasto.

4° corda, 2° tasto   1° e 2° corda aperte, suonate insieme   accordo D aperto

Definizioni Per Annotazioni Speciali Per Chitarra

SEMI-TONO CURVATO: percuotere la nota e curvare di un semitono (1/2 passo).

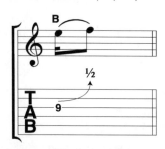

TONO CURVATO: Percuotere la nota e curvare di un tono (passo intero).

NOTA BREVE, CURVATA: percuotere la nota e curvare come indicato. Suonare la prima nota il più velocemente possibile.

QUARTO DI TONO, CURVATO: Percuotere la nota e curvare di un quarto di passo.

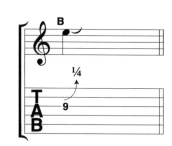

CURVA E LASCIA: Percuotere la nota e curvare come indicato, quindi rilasciare indietro alla nota originale.

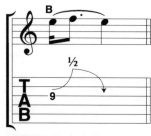

CURVA E RIPERCUOTI: Percuotere la nota e curvare come indicato poi ripercuotere la corda nel punto del simbolo.

PRE-CURVA: Curvare la nota come indicato e quindi percuoterla.

PRE-CURVA E RILASCIO: Curvare la nota come indicato. Colpire e rilasciare la nota indietro alla tonalità indicata.

MARTELLO-COLPISCI: Colpire la prima nota (in basso) con un dito; quindi suona la nota più alta (sulla stessa corda) con un altro dito, toccandola senza pizzicare.

TOGLIERE: Posizionare entrambe le dita sulla nota da suonare. Colpire la prima nota e, senza pizzicare, togliere le dita per suonare la seconda nota (più in basso).

LEGATO SCIVOLATO (GLISSATO): Colpire la prima nota e quindi far scivolare lo stesso dito della mano della tastiera su o giù alla seconda nota. La seconda nota non viene colpita.

CAMBIO SCIVOLATO (GLISSARE E RICOLPIRE): Uguale al legato - scivolato eccetto che viene colpita la seconda nota.

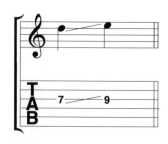

ARMONICA NATURALE: Colpire la nota mentre la mano della tastiera tocca leggermente la corda direttamente sopra il tasto indicato.

PIZZICA E GRAFFIA: Il limite del pizzicato è tirato su (o giù) lungo la corda, producendo un suono graffiante.

SORDINA CON IL PALMO: La nota è parzialmente attenuato dalla mano del pizzicato toccando la corda (le corde) appena prima del ponte.

CORDE SMORZATE: Un suono di percussione viene prodotto appoggiando la mano della tastiera attraverso la corda (le corde) senza premere, e colpendole con la mano del pizzicato.

NOTA: La velocità di ogni curvatura è indicata dalle annotazioni musicali e dal tempo.

Tablatura De Guitarra Explicada

La música de guitarra puede ser representada en tres formas diferentes: en un pentagrama, en tablatura, y con acentos rítmicos.

ACENTOS RITMICOS están escritos sobre el pentagrama. Rasguea los acordes cuando te indique los acentos rítmicos. La aparición de una nota rodeada por un círculo indica una sola nota.

EL PENTAGRAMA muestra la altura y el ritmo y está dividida en compases mediante unas líneas. La altura de las notas se denominan con las siete primeras notas del alfabeto.

TABLATURA representa gráficamente el diapasón de la guitarra. Cada línea horizontal representa una cuerda, y cada número representa un traste.

4ª Cuerda, 2º traste   1ª y 2ª cuerda al aire, tocadas a la vez   Acorde de D abierto

Definiciones Especiales Para La Notacion De Guitarra

BEND DE UN SEMITONO : Ataca la nota y eleva la cuerda hasta que esté medio tono por encima de la nota original (1/2 tono).

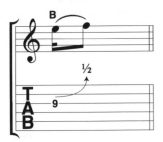

BEND DE UN TONO : Ataca la nota y eleva de la cuerda hasta que esté un tono por encima de la original (un tono completo).

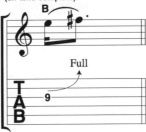

BEND DE UNA NOTA RAPIDA (GRACE NOTE) : Ataca la nota y eleva la cuerda según se indique en la tablatura. Toca la primera nota tan rápidamente como te sea posible.

BEND DE UN CUARTO DE TONO : Ataca la nota y eleva la cuerda hasta que esté un cuarto de tono (1/4 tono) por encima de la original.

BEND & RELEASE : Ataca la nota y eleva la cuerda según se indica en la tablatura, regresa a la posición y nota iniciales.

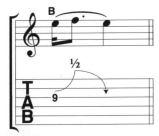

BEND & RESTRIKE: : Ataca la nota y eleva la cuerda según lo que indicado entonces ataca de nuevo la cuerda en la que aparece el símbolo.

PRE-BEND : Eleva la cuerda según lo indicado, después atácala.

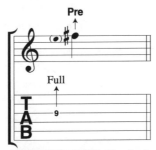

PRE-BEND & RELEASE : Eleva la cuerda según lo indicado. Atácala y regresa a la posición y nota original.

HAMMER-ON : Ataca una nota (grave) con un dedo, entonces haz sonar otra nota más aguda (en la misma cuerda) con otro dedo al tocarla directamente sobre el diapasón, sin atacar la cuerda de nuevo con la púa o los dedos.

PULL-OFF: Sitúa los dedos sobre las notas que desees hacer sonar. Ataca la primera nota y sin utilizar la púa (o los dedos), retira el dedo para hacer que la segunda nota (más grave) suene.

LEGATO SLIDE (GLISS) : Ataca la primera nota y entonces desliza el mismo dedo de la mano situada sobre el diapasón de forma ascendente o descendente hasta alcanzar la segunda nota. La segunda nota no se produce al ser atacada por los dedos o la púa.

SHIFT SLIDE (GLISS & RESTRIKE): Igual que el legato slide, excepto que la segunda nota se ataca con la púa o los dedos.

ARMÓNICOS NATURALES : Ataca la nota mientras que la mano situada sobre el diapasón roza ligeramente la cuerda directamente sobre el traste indicado.

RASPADO DE PÚA : El borde de la púa se desliza de forma descendente (o ascendente) por las cuerdas, provocando un sonido rasposo.

PALM MUTING : La nota es parcialmente apagada al apoyar la mano de la púa ligeramente sobre la cuerdas situándola justo antes del puente.

CUERDAS APAGADAS : Un sonido percusivo que se consigue al apoyar la mano situada sobre el diapasón sobre las cuerda (s) relajando la presión sobre éste, mientras que se ataca (n) con la otra mano.

NOTA : La velocidad de cualquier bend está indicada por la notación musical y el tempo.

CD track listing

1 **tuning notes**

Full instrumental performances (with guitar)...

2 **bodhisattva**
3 **the boston rag**
4 **josie**
5 **kid charlemagne**
6 **reelin' in the years**
7 **rikki don't lose that number**

Backing tracks only (without guitar)...

8 **bodhisattva**
9 **the boston rag**
10 **josie**
11 **kid charlemagne**
12 **reelin' in the years**
13 **rikki don't lose that number**

MCPS

All tracks:
Words & Music by Walter Becker & Donald Fagen
© Copyright Universal/MCA Music Limited.

To remove your CD from the plastic sleeve
lift the small lip to break the perforations
Replace the disc after use for convenient storage

Published by
Wise Publications
14-15 Berners Street, London W1T 3LJ, UK.

Exclusive Distributors:
Music Sales Limited
Distribution Centre, Newmarket Road,
Bury St Edmunds, Suffolk IP33 3YB, UK.

Music Sales Pty Limited
20 Resolution Drive, Caringbah,
NSW 2229, Australia.

Order No. AM965899
ISBN 0-7119-8349-6
This book © Copyright 2001 Wise Publications,
a division of Music Sales Limited.

Music compiled and arranged by Arthur Dick
Music processed by Andrew Shiels
Cover photographs courtesy LFI and Retna

Printed in the EU.

CD recorded by Jonas Persson
All guitars by Arthur Dick
Bass by Paul Townsend
Piano and keyboards by Allan Rogers
Drums by Ian Thomas
Saxophone on 'Josie' by Alex Ward
Guitar preparation by Charlie Chandler at Chandler Guitars

Your Guarantee of Quality
As publishers, we strive to produce
every book to the highest commercial standards.
The music has been freshly engraved and the book has
been carefully designed to minimise awkward page turns
and to make playing from it a real pleasure.
Particular care has been given to specifying acid-free,
neutral-sized paper made from pulps which have not been
elemental chlorine bleached. This pulp is from farmed
sustainable forests and was produced with
special regard for the environment.
Throughout, the printing and binding have been planned
to ensure a sturdy, attractive publication which
should give years of enjoyment.
If your copy fails to meet our high standards,
please inform us and we will gladly replace it.

www.musicsales.com